BEANO®

WHERE'S GNASHER?

STUDIO PRESS

First published in the UK in 2019 by Studio Press Books,
an imprint of Bonnier Books UK,
The Plaza, 535 King's Road,
London, SW10 0SZ

studiopressbooks.co.uk
bonnierbooks.co.uk

Printed in China
1 3 5 7 9 10 8 6 4 2

All rights reserved
ISBN 978-17874-1-514-0

Written by Frankie Jones
Designed by Nia Williams
Illustrated by Laura Howell

GNASHER IS MISSING!

Beanotown is home to many weird and wonderful inhabitants: from the yeti that lives on Mount Beano to the headless headmaster of Horrible Hall, the ghostly librarian and the mysterious tribe of Vikings who founded Beanotown 1,000 years ago. However, there are none weirder or more wonderful than Gnasher, his owner Dennis and their friends and family. Can you track them down as they travel across Beanotown?

GNASHER

This Abyssinian wire-haired tripe hound is Dennis's best friend and partner in crime, and he's gone missing! Gnasher's favourite thing in the world is ~~Dennis~~ sausages. He would do anything for ~~Dennis~~ a delicious sausage.

DENNIS

Dennis is always in trouble – and it's not *always* his fault. If trouble comes knocking, it comes knocking for Dennis. When his best friend Gnasher goes missing, Dennis leads a search party through Beanotown.

MINNIE

Hermione Makepeace, also known as Minnie the Minx, is tougher than all the boys. And smarter. And better looking. Minnie often teams up with her cousin Dennis to cause mischief around Beanotown.

GNIPPER

The only son of the mighty Gnasher, Gnipper is a chip off the old block. He lives with his dad and the Menace family, but is really Bea's best friend and pet.

BEA

This human stink bomb is Dennis's darling little sister. Although she's only just started walking, the littlest Menace loves to help her brother out with all sorts of plots and plans... when she's not filling her nappy.

WALTER

He might be Dennis's next-door neighbour and classmate, but there's nothing friendly about Walter. Walter hates anything that's fun, because he's far too sophisticated for that.

LOCATIONS

Welcome to this pleasant, quiet town where citizens walk the streets free from the fear of pranks, monsters and chaos. Oh, wait! I'm mistaken. This is Beanotown – where chaos rules supreme and a boy named Dennis has lost Gnasher, his dog. Search the pages to see if you can find the Abyssinian wire-haired tripe hound affectionately known as Gnasher, as well as Dennis, Minnie, Gnipper, Walter and Bea. At the back of the book there's a super-long list of other Beano characters and objects to search for. I dare you to find them all!

51 GASWORKS ROAD

BASH STREET SCHOOL

THE BEANOTOWN TUNNELS

BEANOTOWN PARK

DUCK ISLAND

BEANOTOWN HIGH STREET

4

THE TOWN HALL

BEANOTOWN LIBRARY

BEANOTOWN MUSEUM

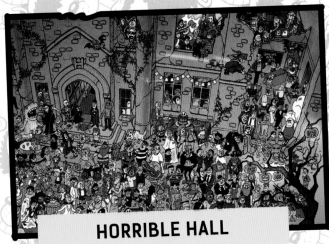

HORRIBLE HALL

MOUNT BEANO

BEANOTOWN ZOO

BEANOTOWN BEACH

BEANOTOWN POLICE STATION

51 Gasworks Road: home to the Menace family. Today it's Dennis Senior's birthday. He didn't want to have a party, but Gran made a cake and it seems like the whole town turned up for a slice, including some familiar faces. In the free-for-all cake scrum Dennis has lost sight of Gnasher. Can you spot this unspotted dog?

Bash Street School: a place of learning, discipline and respect. That is, until it's lunchtime. The Bash Street Kids have started a food fight – and you'd better watch out because Olive and Olive (the dinner ladies) make rock cakes that are... well... like rocks. Can you see Gnasher between the flying food?

The Beanotown Tunnels are as mysterious as they are vast and run deep beneath the school. These caverns and passageways hold many treasures and secrets: for example, the intriguing carvings that look like ancient Menace graffiti; and a clockwork robot that looks strangely familiar. Perhaps Gnasher is seeking out a bone to gnaw?

Beanotown Park is the place to go for outdoor activities like playing football, picnicking with friends, going on the swings, discovering a Spring of Not Really Youth, being chased by a yeti in the woods... actually maybe don't go into the woods. I also heard there's a sausage-obsessed dog stealing everyone's snacks and frisbees.

Duck Island is the strangest place in Beanotown, and that's saying something. What appears to be a small island in the middle of the park's pond is actually a huge island, home to many peculiar characters. Look out for a tribe of Vikings, avoid the man-eating plants, never, ever make eye contact with the T. rex, and if you see Gnasher, tell him Dennis is looking for him.

Beanotown High Street isn't like a usual high street. If you want a new pair of shoes, a present for your gran or dishwashing tablets, you might want to go somewhere else. If you want the latest pranking gadget, the most sausage-y sausages or a jumper knitted from the wool of a red mountain goat, Beanotown High Street has you covered. Now, where could Gnasher be hiding?

The Town Hall is the place where Beanotown policy is made. Like Mayor Wilbur Brown's policy of no **fun**kiness on a Wednesday, or of no **fun**fairs, or of no **fun** whatsoever. Not many people know that the clock tower on top is a time machine. Perhaps Gnasher has somehow transported himself back in time? Look out for Dennis's mutt in the crowd!

Beanotown Library contains books, just like any other library, but some of those books are a little odd. The library also contains a ghostly librarian who looks after the strangest tomes. Beware of what you pull off the shelf – sometimes you might get an unwanted surprise! If you're looking for Gnasher, start at 'A' and work your way along the shelves.

NEW BOOKS

MEET the AUTHOR!

GRAPHIC NOVELS

COOKERY

FICTION

ART

ENQUIRIES

Beanotown Museum is as confusing as it is educational. Sure, it has historical artefacts and those little plaques with tiny writing telling you about what the object is, where it was found, blah, blah, blah... but the exhibits are all quite unusual. Must-sees include Thor's Toothpick and a copy of the very first Beano annual! Amongst all this strangeness, can you see Gnasher?

MITTEN OF DOOM

"BILLY", THE WORLD'S FASTEST DINOSAUR

Horrible Hall was the school in Beanotown until it was destroyed. It's where Dennis's gran learnt everything she knows. Legend says that the Headless Headmaster haunts Horrible Hall (try saying that quickly three times whilst standing on one leg), but seeing is believing. Everyone is in costume for Halloween. What's Gnasher dressed as?

APPLE BOBBING

Mount Beano, the mighty, snow-capped peak, offers the citizens of Beanotown year-round skiing as it has its own microclimate (that means it snows even in a heatwave!). This is great for Mr Frosty the snowman but not such good news for Dennis who is still looking for Gnasher. He should be easy to spot against all that white snow!

Beanotown Zoo and its zookeepers are leaders in animal conservation. It's just a shame that they can't seem to conserve the animals within their enclosures. There are daily escapes and citizens of Beanotown are used to seeing an elephant walking past the school, or a troop of monkeys outside the greengrocer's. Maybe Gnasher is hiding here, looking for some canine company.

AQUARIUM

DO NOT FEED THE WOLVES

DO NOT EAT THE HUMANS

Beanotown Beach isn't quite a postcard-perfect seaside escape, but there is sand and sea for those who like to sunbathe and splash! Swimmers must always beware of creatures lurking beneath the waves, and anyone wanting to sail into Beanotown should look out for the black beam emitted from the lighthouse. No time to stop for an ice cream... Gnasher's still missing!

Beanotown Police Station is where you will find the sneakiest, meanest characters Beanotown has to offer – and that's just the police officers! You might also meet some hardened criminals like General Blight and Dr Gloom locked in the cells. It looks like Gnasher's trail has led us all the way here, but can you spot him and reunite Dennis with his best friend?

THINKING OF BREAKING THE LAW? DON'T!

EVIDENCE

EXHIBIT 'A'

33

WANT MORE FUN? TRY FINDING THESE HIDDEN CHARACTERS AND OBJECTS!

51 Gasworks Road
- Dennis's Dad
- Dennis's Mum
- A black-and-red wrapped present
- Sergeant Slipper
- A gnome with a green hat
- A pink cupcake

Duck Island
- A triceratops
- A lost frisbee
- A thirsty man-eating plant
- Two fighter pilots
- A duck
- A T. rex

Bash Street School
- Teacher
- A green squelchy
- A science book
- Olive 1
- Olive 2
- A red rucksack

Beanotown High Street
- A whoopee cushion
- A postbox
- A squelchy with a hat
- Roger the Dodger
- A statue wearing a traffic cone
- A flowery shopping bag

The Beanotown Tunnels
- A golden peashooter
- A lost snorkeller
- A Viking shield
- Calamity James
- A mechanical Walter
- A set of false teeth

The Town Hall
- Future Dennis
- A lie detector
- Foo Foo the poodle
- The Mayor's missing chain
- An ice lolly
- A red skateboard

Beanotown Park
- A yeti
- A missing drone
- A tyre swing
- Billy Whizz
- A mole
- JJ

Beanotown Library
- A stolen love story
- A Beano author
- A bookworm
- Minnie's lost library card
- Les Pretend
- A stack of Beano annuals

Beanotown Museum
🐾 An antique sock
🐾 Thor's Toothpick
🐾 Toots
🐾 A bag of stolen gold
🐾 A sleepy security guard
🐾 A mummy

Horrible Hall
🐾 The Headless Headmaster
🐾 Betty and Yeti in costume
🐾 A cyclops
🐾 A portrait of Walter's grandfather
🐾 A torch
🐾 A two-headed worm

Mount Beano
🐾 A snow Gnasher
🐾 Rodney the Red Ram
🐾 A campfire
🐾 A polka-dot scarf
🐾 A hot chocolate
🐾 Tricky Dicky

Beanotown Zoo
🐾 Big Eggo
🐾 Pink candyfloss
🐾 Roger the Dodger
🐾 An escaping gorilla
🐾 An unusual zookeeper
🐾 The zookeeper's missing keys

Beanotown Beach
🐾 Pirates' treasure
🐾 A cat
🐾 Billy Whizz
🐾 A snorkeller
🐾 A red-and-black striped towel
🐾 A lost penguin

Beanotown Police Station
🐾 A crowbar
🐾 Dr Gloom
🐾 A box of doughnuts
🐾 An escape route
🐾 A confiscated catapult
🐾 Stolen sausages

ANSWERS

Dennis, Gnasher, Minnie, Gnipper, Walter and Bea are circled in yellow, and the other characters and objects to search and find are circled in red. Did you find them all?

51 GASWORKS ROAD

BASH STREET SCHOOL

THE BEANOTOWN TUNNELS

BEANOTOWN PARK

DUCK ISLAND

BEANOTOWN HIGH STREET

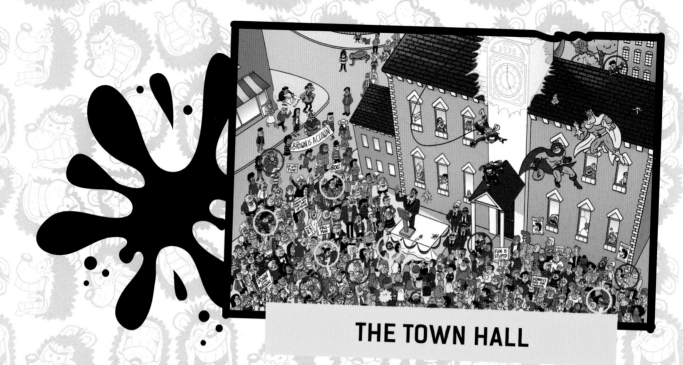

THE TOWN HALL

BEANOTOWN LIBRARY

BEANOTOWN MUSEUM

HORRIBLE HALL

MOUNT BEANO

BEANOTOWN ZOO

BEANOTOWN BEACH

BEANOTOWN POLICE STATION

THE GANG